The Highland cattle

Written by Jill Atkins

Illustrated by Shelagh McNicholas

Heinemann

In the summer Alison went to stay
with her gran and grandad in
Scotland. One day Alison looked
out of the window. She could see some
Highland cattle in a field. They were
very big and had long horns.

Then she saw two big boys by
the gate. The boys opened the gate
and went into the field.
'What are they doing?' said Alison.

Just then she heard her gran calling,
'Time for tea, Alison.'
Alison went down the stairs as fast
as she could.

She ran over to
the table and
sat down so fast
that her tea went
everywhere.

'Alison! You mustn't run about in the house,' said Gran. 'You had better go out to play when you've had your tea.'

So after tea Alison went to see Jamie,
the boy who lived next door.
'Can you come out to play?' she asked.
'Yes,' said Jamie. 'We could go up to
the farm to see the Highland cattle.'
'I'm scared of them,' said Alison.
'I don't like the look of their long
horns, but I'll still come with you.'

As Alison and Jamie walked up to
the farm they saw a cow on the road.
'How did you get out?' said Jamie.
'It must have been the boys I saw,'
said Alison. 'They forgot to shut
the gate.'

Just then they saw lots more cows
coming out of the field.
'Let's go home,' said Alison.
'No, we must help the farmer,'
said Jamie. 'I'll go and tell him.'
'I'll come with you,' said Alison.
'No,' said Jamie. 'You stay here.
You'll have to look after the cows.'

Jamie ran off to get
the farmer.
'I'm scared of cows!'
shouted Alison.
But Jamie had gone.

Alison looked at the cow and the
cow looked at Alison.

Then she saw a stick on the ground.
Alison waved it at the cow. The cow
stayed very still.

'Shoo!' said Alison, waving the stick.
'Moo!' went the cow, and it turned
and went back into the field.

Alison waved her stick at another cow.
'Go back!' she said. 'Please go back!'
And that cow went back into the field.
'I'm not so scared now,' said Alison,
and she waved her stick again and
again. She made all the cows go back
into the field.

When the last cow was in the field
Alison shut the gate. She saw
Jamie and the farmer coming down
the road.

'Where have all the cows gone?'
asked Jamie.

'How did they all get back in the
field?' asked the farmer.

Alison showed them the stick.

'I asked them nicely,' she said.

'You did very well,' said the farmer.

'Let's go and tell your gran.'

So they all went back to Gran's
cottage. The farmer told Gran how
Alison got all the cows back into
the field.

'Were you scared?' asked Gran as she
gave Alison a big hug.

'Well, maybe just a little,' said Alison.

The next day
Gran asked Alison
if she wanted to
go for a walk.
They set off down
the road and
came to the field
with the gate.

'Let's go through the field,' said Alison.
'No,' said Gran, 'I don't think
we should.'

'Gran, are you scared of the cows?'
said Alison.

'Well, maybe just a little,' said Gran.

'Well, I'm not scared any more,' said
Alison. 'I'll look after you.'